CW00956642

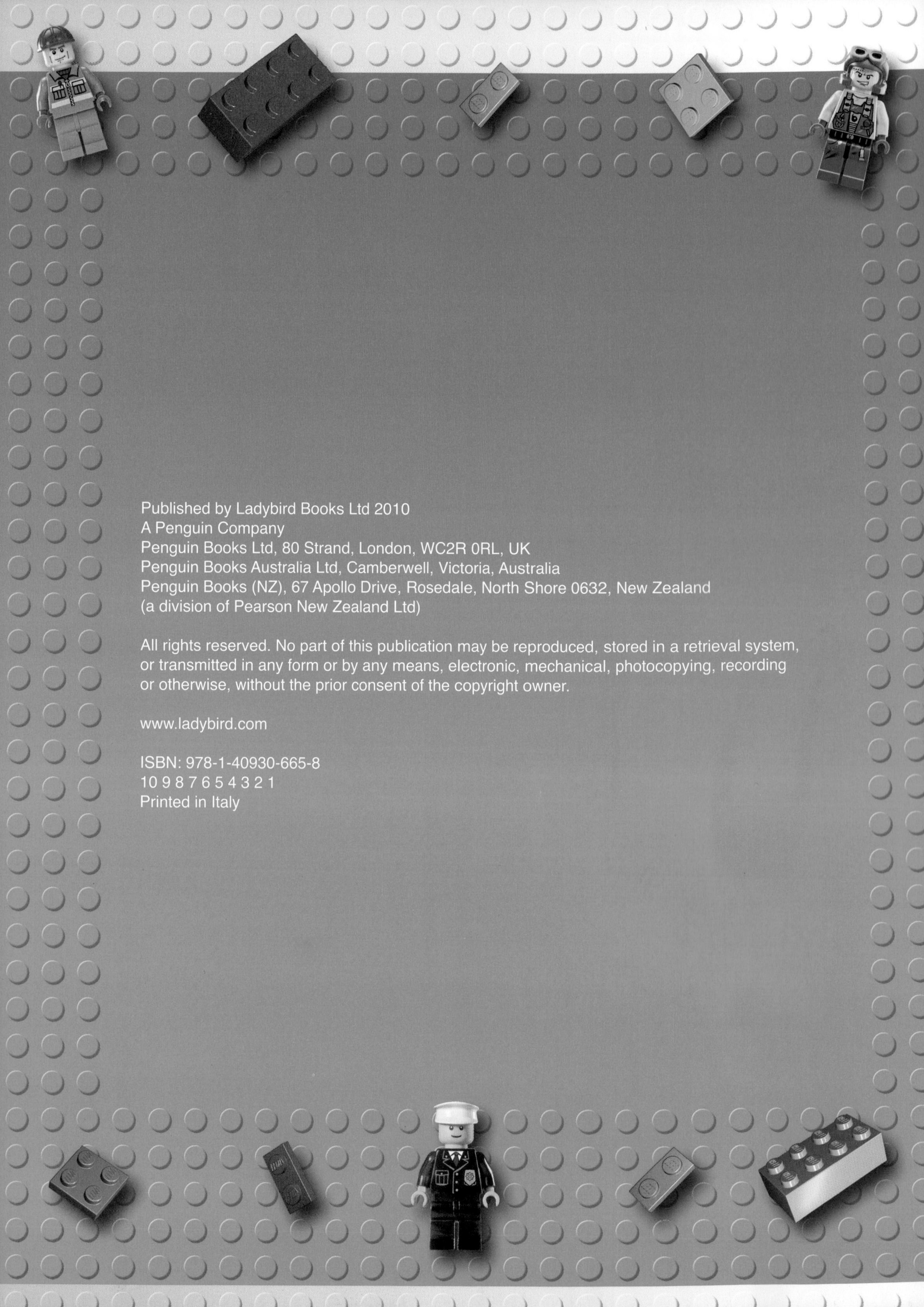

Published by Ladybird Books Ltd 2010
A Penguin Company
Penguin Books Ltd, 80 Strand, London, WC2R 0RL, UK
Penguin Books Australia Ltd, Camberwell, Victoria, Australia
Penguin Books (NZ), 67 Apollo Drive, Rosedale, North Shore 0632, New Zealand
(a division of Pearson New Zealand Ltd)

www.ladybird.com

ISBN: 978-1-40930-665-8
10 9 8 7 6 5 4 3 2 1
Printed in Italy

THE OFFICIAL LEGO® ANNUAL 2011

CONTENTS

Garage Tidy-Up

Help the mechanics tidy up the garage! Look at the spare parts at the bottom of the page and count how many of each one you can find in the picture.

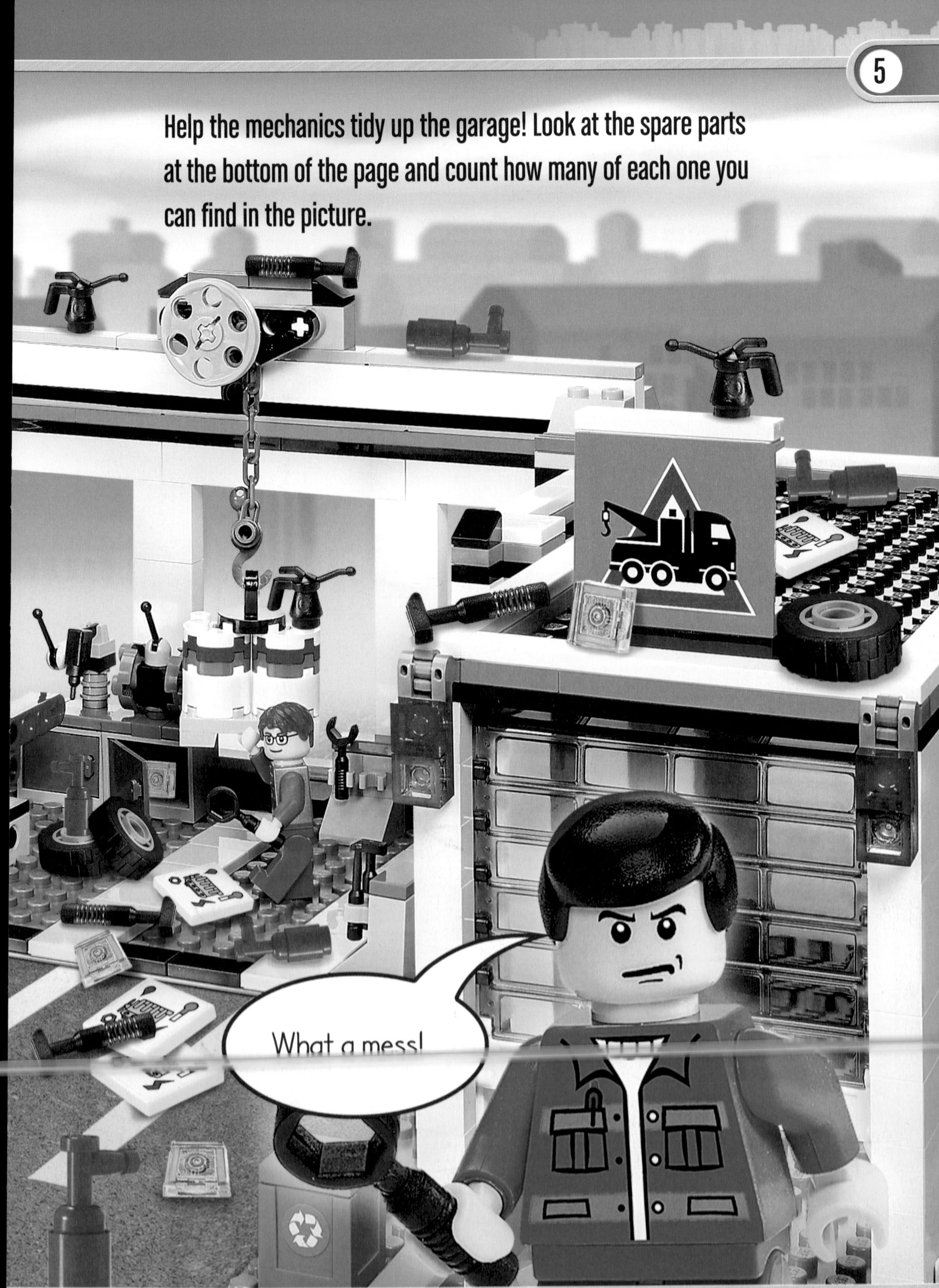

Risky Flight

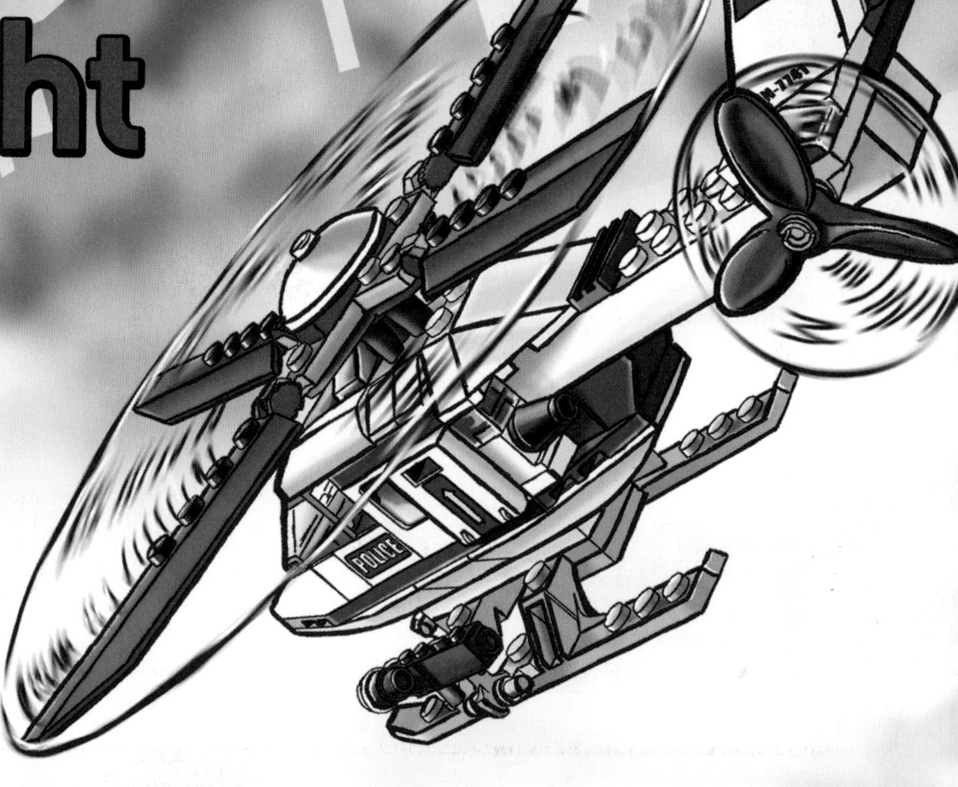

This helicopter is lost in the fog! Starting from the red square, use the navigation system commands to guide it safely to land on top of the skyscraper!

Police Business

The police are looking for two bank robbers in this line-up. The witnesses report that the robbers escaped through a small back door - only 160 cm high - without ducking! And they were both missing a tooth. Which of the suspects are the bank robbers?

Fire Alarm!

Guide the fire engine through the city maze to the fire. Be careful though - some streets are blocked!

HA 7208

Draw a LEGO® Fireman!

1. Start with four basic shapes.

2. Round off the corners of the head and add a stud on top. Draw the neck and the waist. Then, add the arms and some hands shaped like pincers.

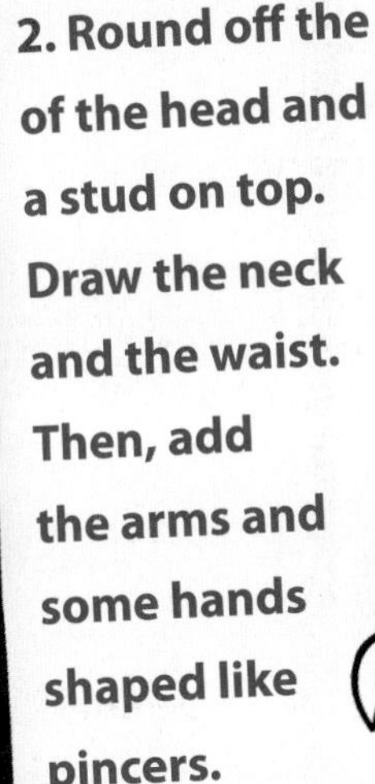

3. It's time for the details! Add buttons and badges – and why not give your minifigure a funny expression? Remember: the eyes should be simple black dots, and minifigures do not have noses or ears.

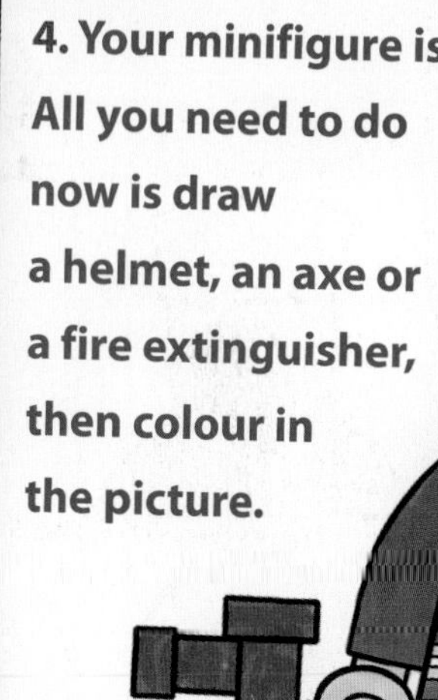

4. Your minifigure is almost ready. All you need to do now is draw a helmet, an axe or a fire extinguisher, then colour in the picture.

City Sudoku

Complete this picture sudoku using the spare minifigures. Each row, column and 2x2 box must contain each picture only once. Write the correct letters in the blank spaces to finish the grid!

True or False?

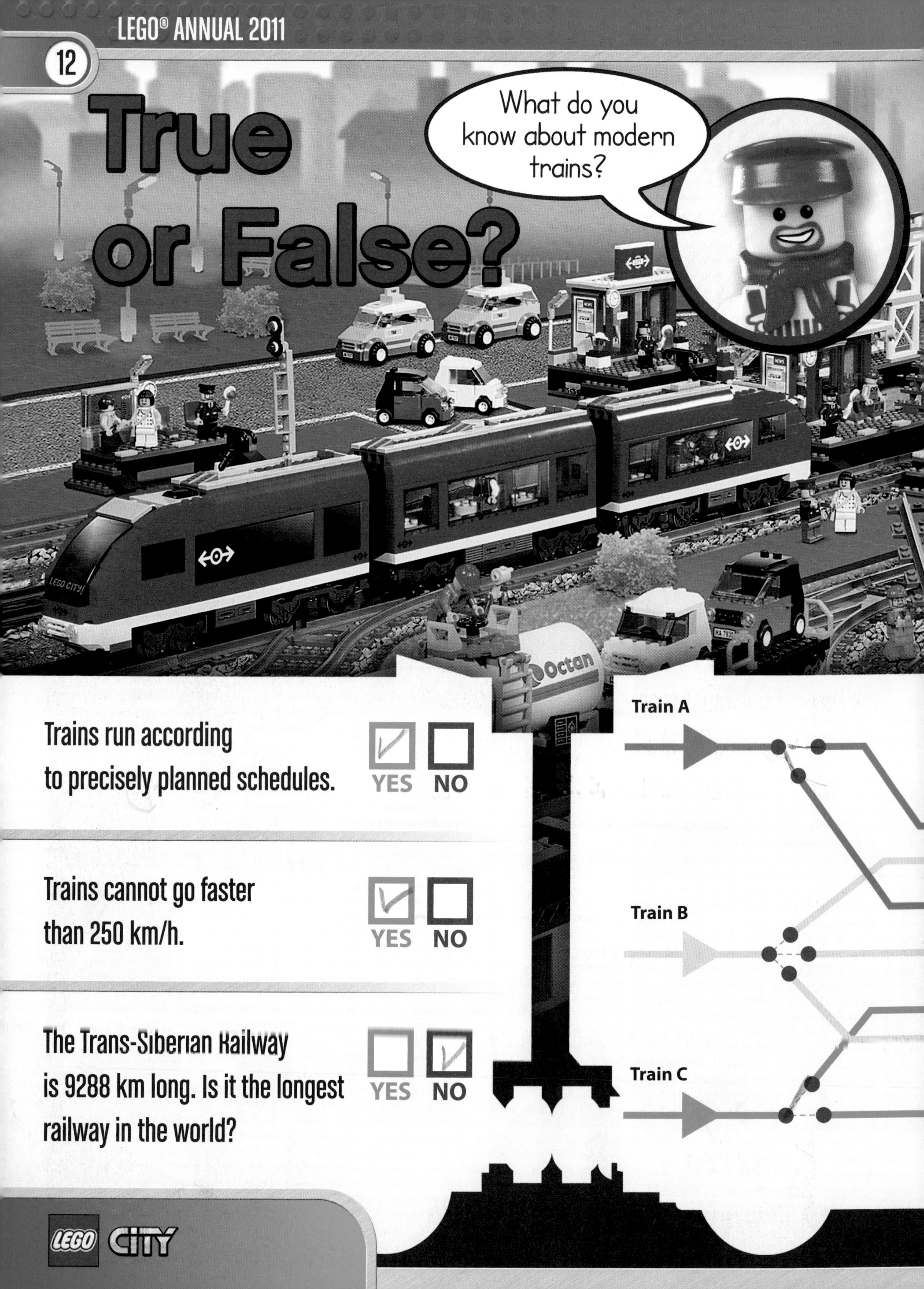

Trains run according to precisely planned schedules. YES NO

Trains cannot go faster than 250 km/h. YES NO

The Trans-Siberian Railway is 9288 km long. Is it the longest railway in the world? YES NO

Off We Go!

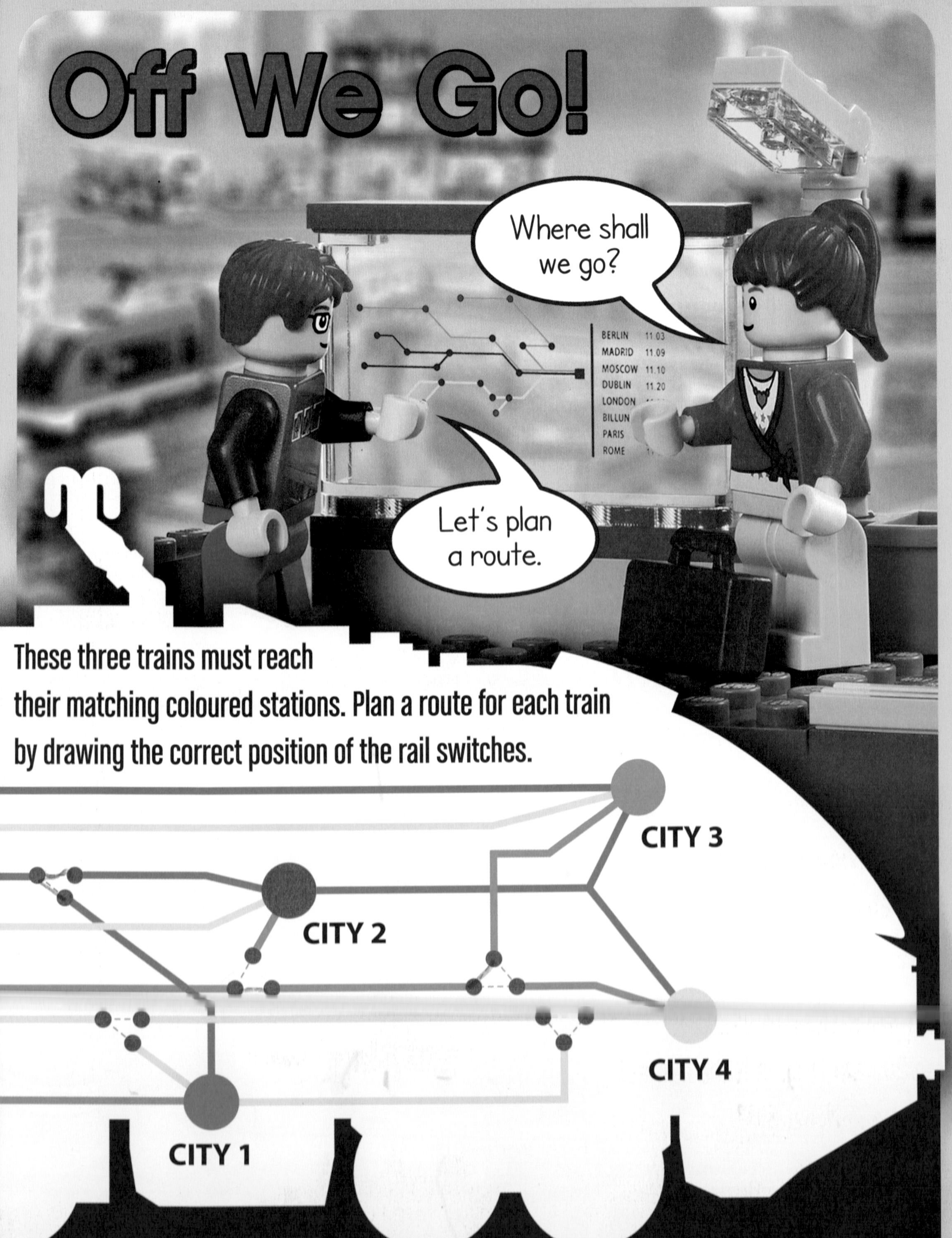

These three trains must reach their matching coloured stations. Plan a route for each train by drawing the correct position of the rail switches.

DIY Bike

Help the mechanics finish building this bicycle using the spare parts. The number on each part indicates how many times you can use it and you can rotate the parts if you need to. Draw them in with a pen!

2x

1x

1x
1x
SHOP

Pirate Code

Yo ho ho! Use the code to decipher this cryptic message and find out which direction you need to sail to get to the pirate treasure!

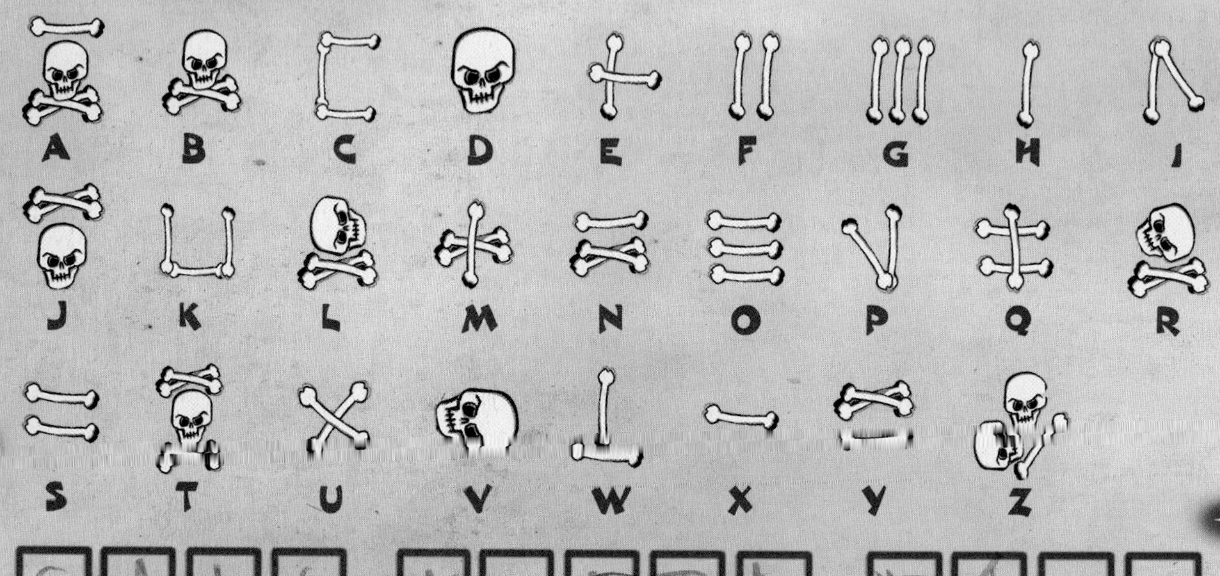

Treasure Hunt

Shiver me timbers, let's find the buried treasure! Follow the clues to draw a path on the map below, then mark an 'X' where you find the booty.

- Starting at the tallest palm tree, count 6 squares up.
- Move 4 squares left, behind the pile of skulls.
- Move 4 squares down to the pirate flag, then move back again by 2 squares to find where the treasure is buried!

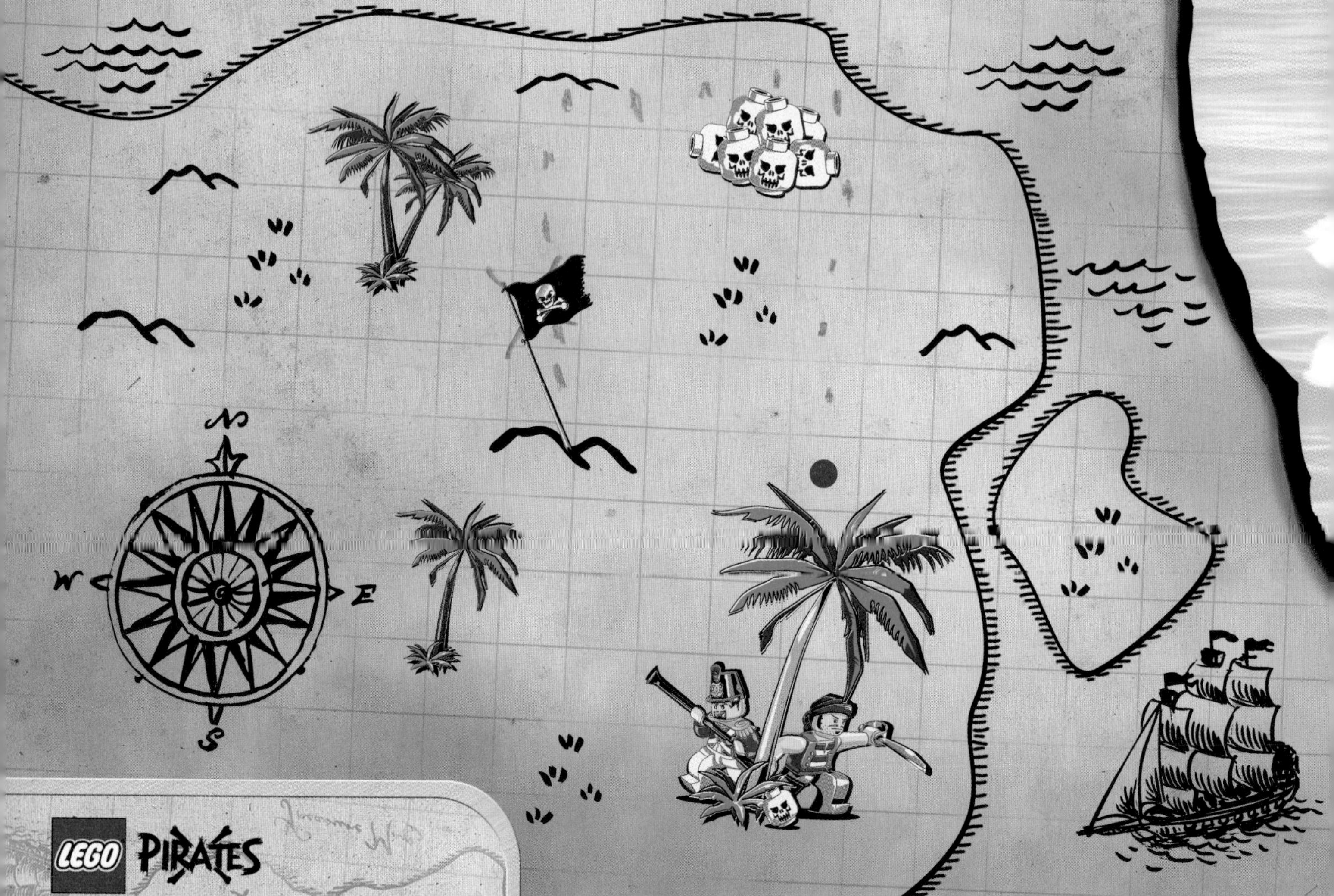

N
W
E
S

How Heavy?

This pirate has a hook for sale! He wants to sell it for as many coins as it weighs. Look at the scales below and work out how many coins equal the weight of one hook.

Octopus Riddles

This octopus has snatched four things from the pirates with his tentacles. Can you match the objects to their rightful owners? Write the correct numbers in the empty boxes.

I can't see what's on the horizon without it!
It's made of steel.
You shoot with it.
It's made of gold.

Cannonball Conundrum

This soldier is extremely punctual. He shoots his cannon at the same times every day. Can you work out when he will fire next? Circle the correct cannonball in the pile below.

Jolly Roger!

Complete the pirate flag! Draw the other half of the skull using the guidelines.

Who's Missing?

The minifigures had their photo taken – but the photographer wanted to be in it too! You can see him in the back row. Who took the picture instead? Circle the person missing from the photograph.

Who Am I?

This witch is late for a big costume ball and she can't find her date! She doesn't know what his costume looks like, but she has a note with a few clues. Can you help her find him?

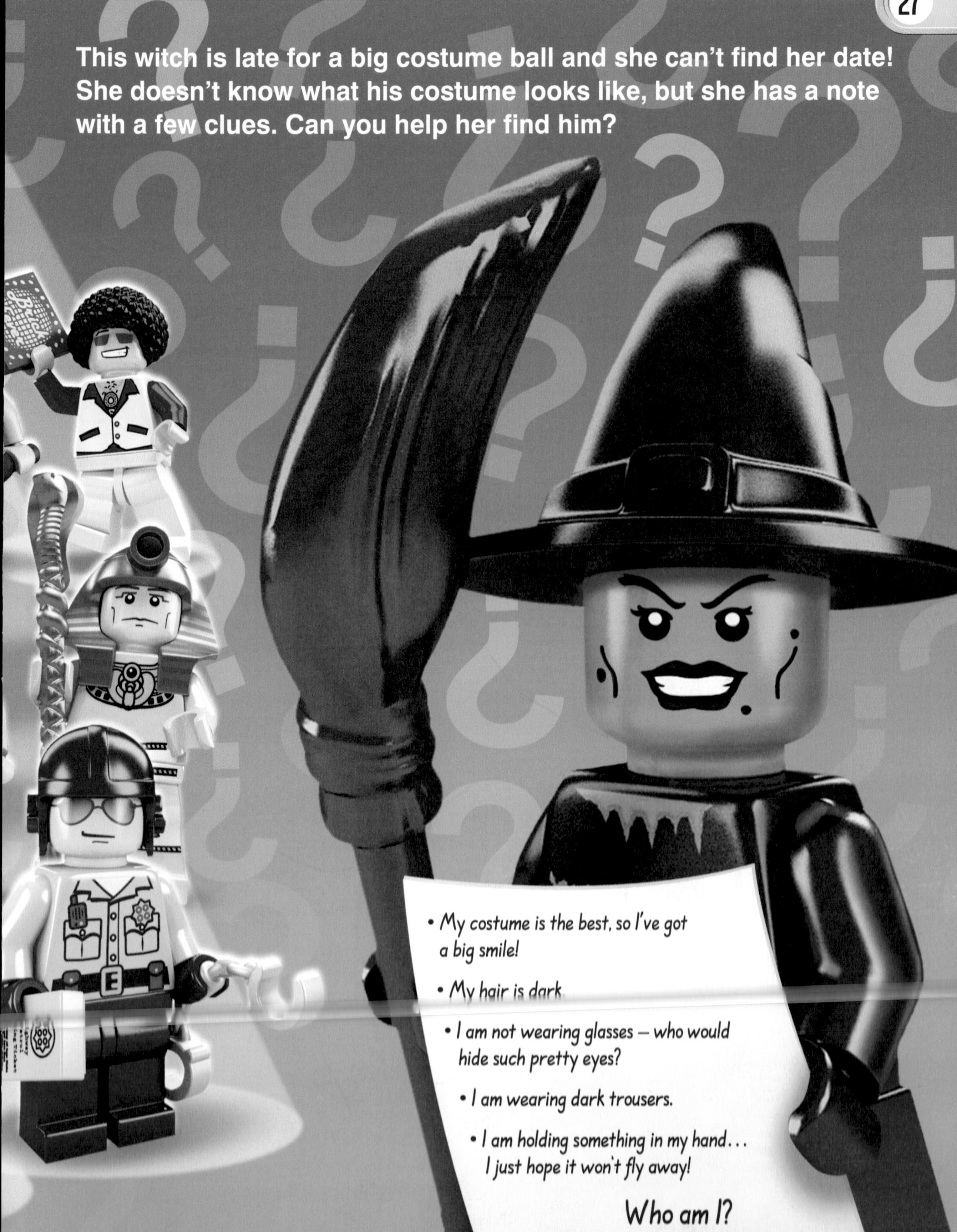

- *My costume is the best, so I've got a big smile!*
- *My hair is dark.*
- *I am not wearing glasses – who would hide such pretty eyes?*
- *I am wearing dark trousers.*
- *I am holding something in my hand... I just hope it won't fly away!*

Who am I?

Puzzle Cube

Look at the cubes below.
Two cubes are missing
a picture on one side.
Can you work out which of
the numbered pictures should
go on the blank sides?

1

2

3

4

5

6

Odd One Out

One minifigure in each row below is different to the others. Circle the odd one out!

PICTURE SPOT

The Power Miners are digging for precious crystals. They just have to watch out for the hungry lava monsters! Only one of the small pictures belongs to the big picture. Which one?

COOL DRINKS

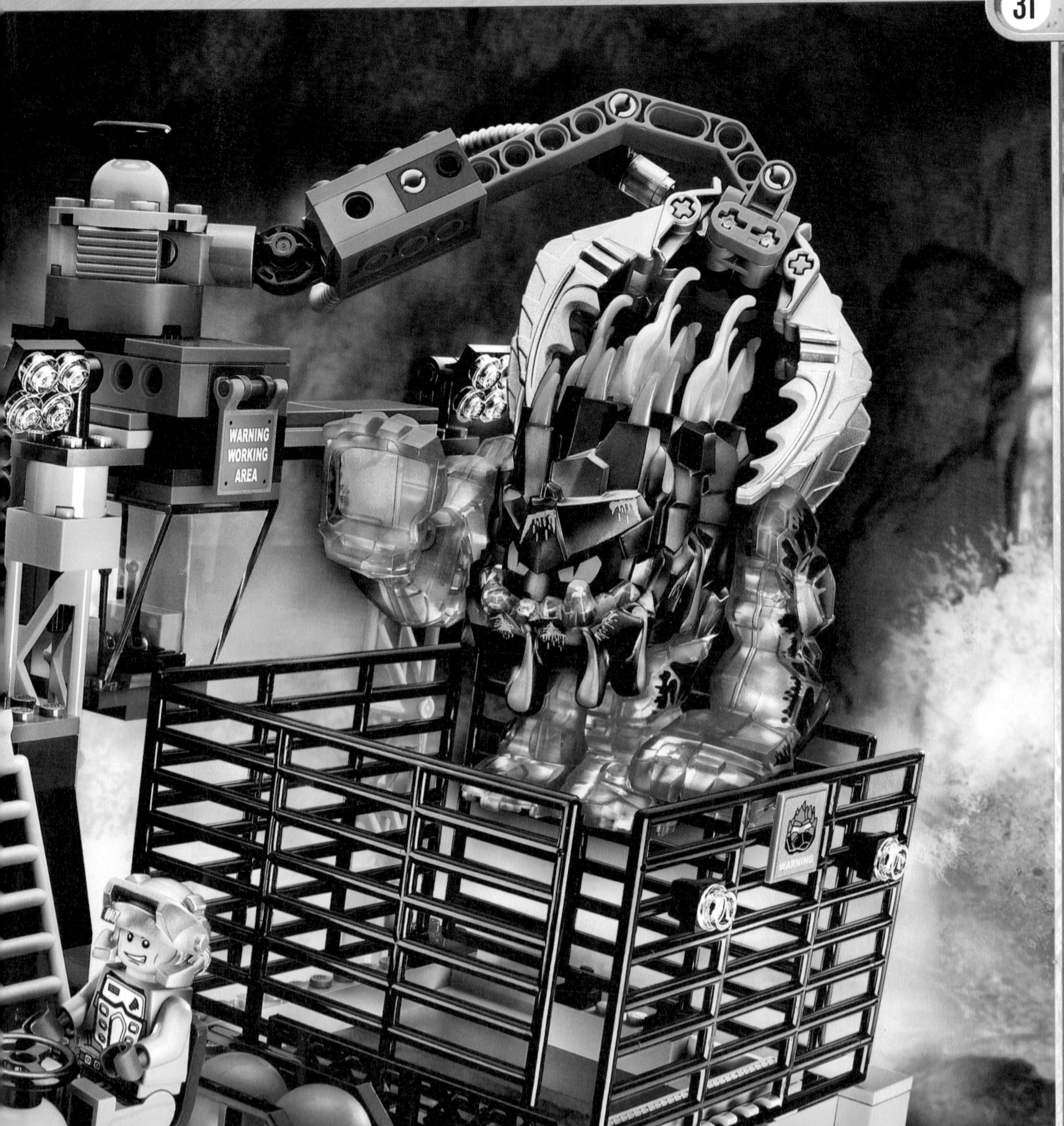

WARNING
WORKING
AREA

WARNING

A

B

C

D

WARNING

WARNING
KING
AREA

CRYSTAL STORY

Brains is telling Doc a story, but he's getting all muddled up! Can you help put the story in the right order by completing the letters in his speech bubble?

1	2	3	4	5
A				B

C

D
KNOCK!
KNOCK!
KNOCK!

E

ROCKY CHASE

Who will catch the lava monster first? Add up the numbers along each line below – the Power Miner with the lowest number is the fastest!

5 8 6 12 31

7 8 11 3 29

3 1 2 5 11

7 6 5 4 22

WHAT'S NEXT?

Which picture should come next in each of the columns below? Choose the correct letter to complete each sequence.

BLUE CRYSTAL RACE

PLAYER 1 PLAYER 2 PLAYER 3 PLAYER 4

START

How to Play:
A game for 2-4 players. Find a die and use the bricks from the cover of this book as counters. Decide who will go first, then take turns to roll the die and move across the board. Just be careful what you land on! Follow the instructions every time you step on a picture circle. The first player to reach the finish wins. Good luck, miners!

FINISH

SPECIAL FIELDS

LAVA MONSTER
A nasty monster has damaged your vehicle. Wait one turn until you fix it.

CRYSTAL
Jump forward three spaces.

DYNAMITE
Blast your way through a rock wall. Go two steps back and hide before it explodes!

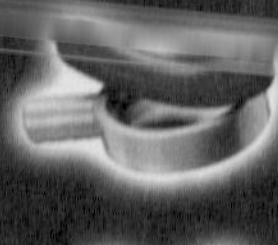

SAUSAGE
Feeling hungry? Time to grab a bite... but you miss one turn.

TWIN CATAPULT
Double acceleration! Move forward the same number of spaces again.

CRYSTAL KING
You can't get past the king of the lava monsters! Go back to the start.

SUBMARINE SHADOWS

The ATLANTIS Deep Sea Salvage Crew have fantastic subs in their small fleet. The Typhoon Turbo Sub, built by Professor Sam Rhodes, is incredibly fast and agile – plus it looks really great! Which shadow matches the Typhoon's shape?

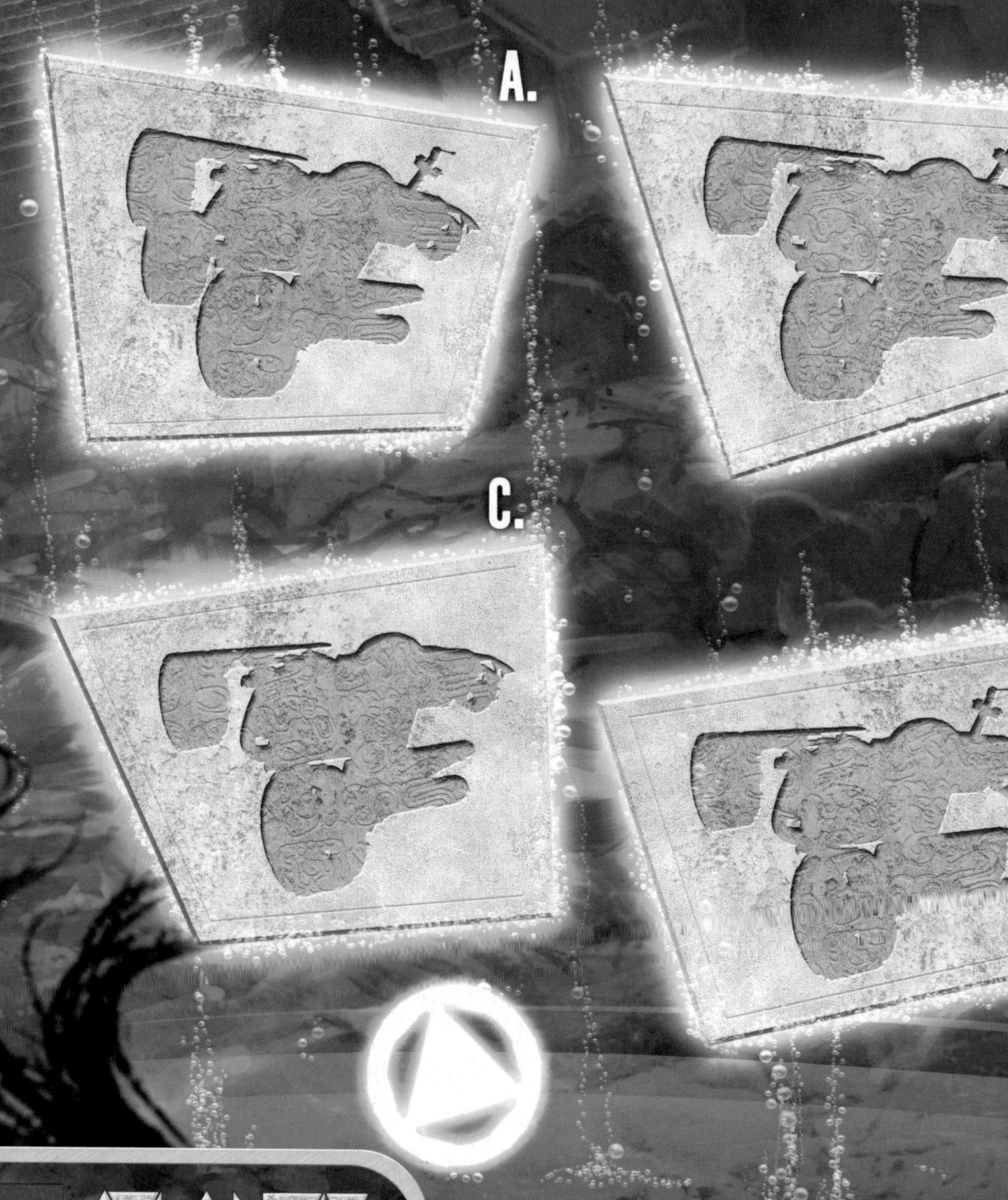

SPOT THE DIFFERENCE

Terrible monsters lurk in the dark depths of the ocean. They guard precious crystals – the keys to the Portal of Atlantis. Look carefully at these two pictures of the divers fighting the Scorpion Guardian. Can you find five differences between them?

WARRIOR COUNT

The evil Portal Emperor will do anything to stop the intruders entering the Portal of Atlantis. Now he's sent an army of sea warriors to attack them! How many warriors of each species are there in the picture?

ATLANTIS SEARCH

Look carefully at this picture of the Portal of Atlantis. One of the small images on the right does not belong to the big picture – but which one?

1
2
3
4
5
6

UNDERWATER DOMINOES

Look carefully at the domino chain. Which of the spare dominoes will complete it? Write the correct letters in the blank spaces!

A NEW HERO

Hero Factory designs and builds robot heroes who fight evil in every corner of the universe. How about drawing a hero of your own design in the space below?

HERO LINE-UP

The heroes' armour and equipment are fitted for all kinds of missions. Look at the small pictures at the bottom of the page. Can you match each picture to the correct hero? Watch out! Two pictures don't belong to any of them...

5
6
7
8

KNOW YOUR FOE

They create havoc and mayhem. They steal and destroy. They are a threat to the universe! Match each description to the correct villain and write their names in the blank spaces.

A

His lethal staff can create black holes and his vicious black spiky armour is enough to scare enemies to death!

B

His huge claws and corrosive spit can cause major damage, but his favourite weapon is the horn on his green armoured head!

CORRODER

THUNDER

C

His arrival is announced by a deafening rumble... and then he wreaks havoc with his giant crusher claw and blaster.

D

The two tanks on his shoulders are full of toxic waste which this one-eyed wretch fires at his enemies.

XPLODE

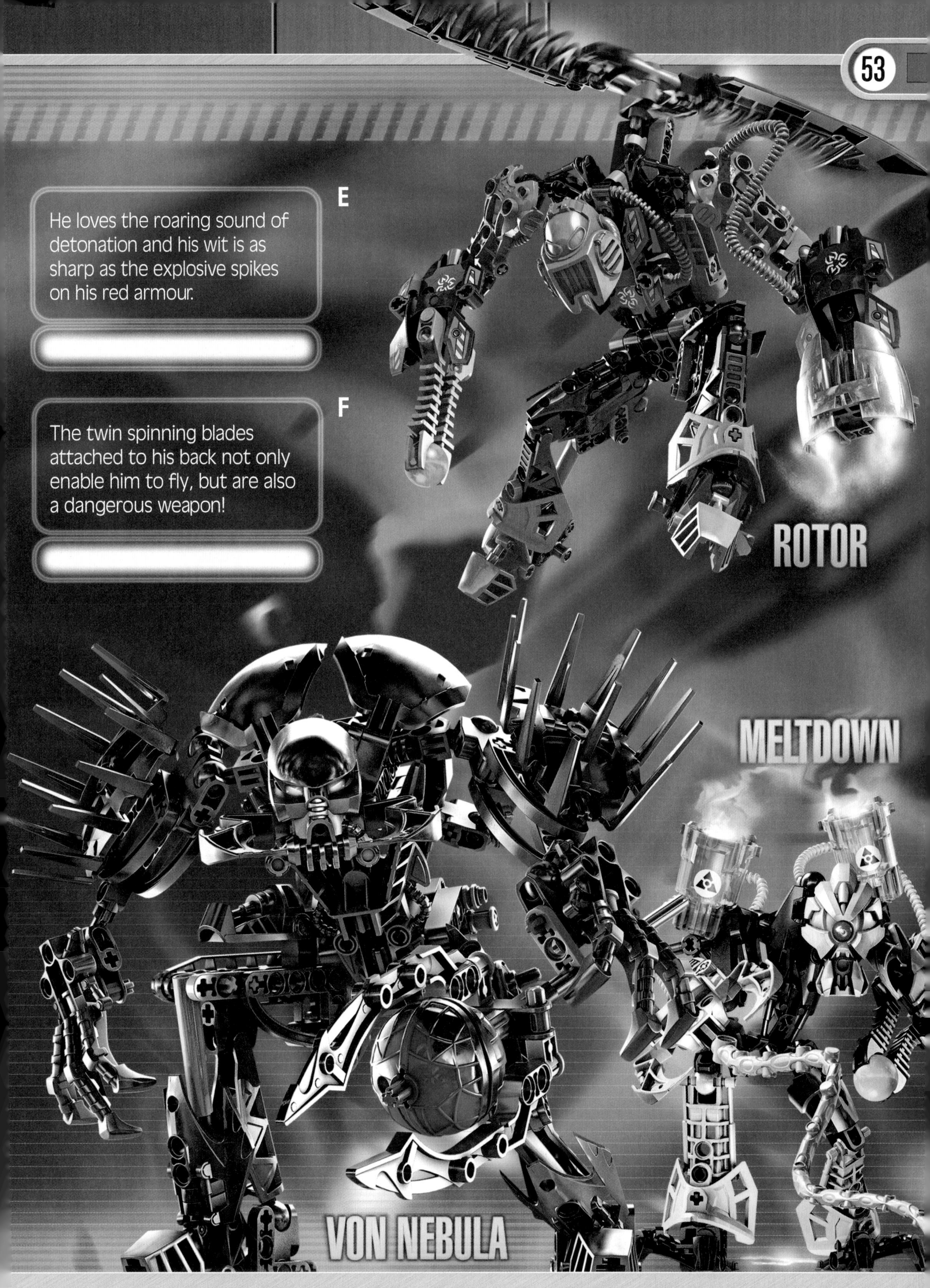
E
He loves the roaring sound of detonation and his wit is as sharp as the explosive spikes on his red armour.
F
The twin spinning blades attached to his back not only enable him to fly, but are also a dangerous weapon!
ROTOR
MELTDOWN
VON NEBULA

THE LAST DETAIL

Look at these pictures showing William Furno fighting two mighty villains. Can you spot one tiny difference between the two images? Hurry, before the Hero Factory Air Command's drop ship arrives to back Furno up!

Page 4
Garage Tidy-Up

Page 6
Risky Flight

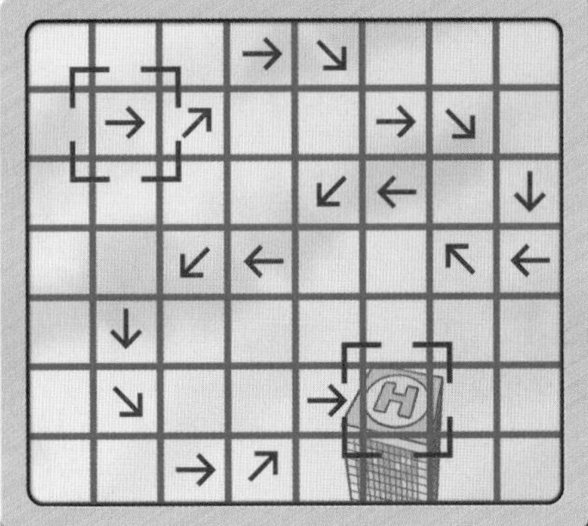

Page 7
Police Business
B and D

Page 8
Fire Alarm!

Page 11
City Sudoku

Page 12
True or False?

Page 13
Off We Go!

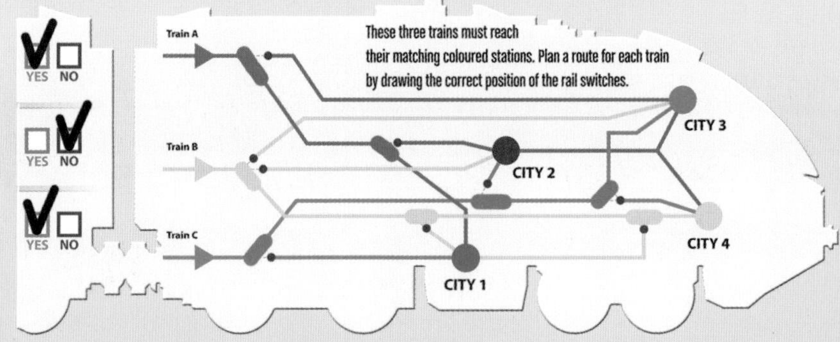

Page 14
DIY Bike

answers

Page 16
Pirate Code
SAIL NORTH EAST

Page 18
Treasure Hunt

Page 19
How Heavy?
2 coins

Page 20
Octopus Riddles
4 I can't see what's on the horizon without it!

1 It's made of gold.

3 You shoot with it.

2 It's made of steel.

Page 22
Cannonball Conundrum
10.00

Page 24
Who's Missing?

Page 26

Who Am I?

Page 28
Puzzle Cube

Page 29

Odd One Out

row 1 row 2 row 3

Page 30
PICTURE SPOT
D

Page 32
CRYSTAL STORY
1 – A, 2 – C, 3 – E, 4 – D, 5 – B

Page 34
ROCKY CHASE
8+7+11+3=29

5+8+6+12=31

3+2+1+5=11

7+6+5+4=22

Page 35
WHAT'S NEXT?
B, A, D

answers

Page 38
SUBMARINE SHADOWS
B

Page 40
SPOT THE DIFFERENCE

Page 44
ATLANTIS SEARCH

Page 42
WARRIOR COUNT

Page 48
WHO DO YOU CALL?
1-800-HERO

Page 46
UNDERWATER DOMINOES

Page 50
HERO LINE-UP

Page 52
KNOW YOUR FOE

A: VON NEBULA
B: CORRODER
C: THUNDER
D: MELTDOWN
E: XPLODE
F: ROTOR

Page 54
THE LAST DETAIL

Collect these other great LEGO® books!

ISBN: 9781409306276
RRP: £4.99

With cool LEGO® Atlantis minifigures!

ISBN: 9781409306269
RRP: £4.99

Coming soon!

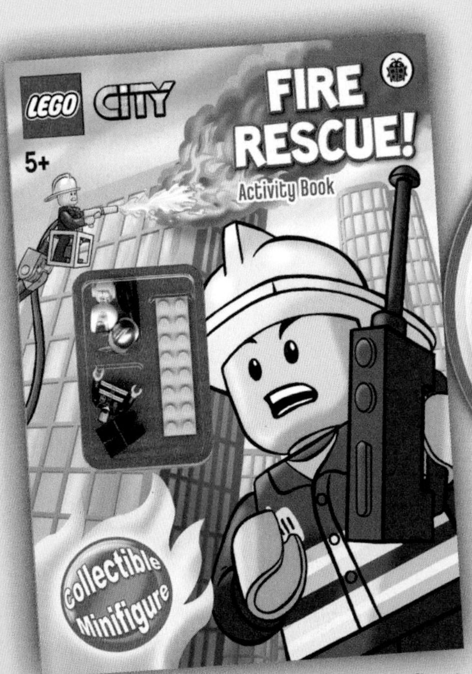

*art not final

ISBN: 9781409308041
RRP: £4.99

With awesome LEGO® City minifigures!

LEGO CITY LET'S BUILD! 5+ Activity Book Collectible minifigure

*art not final

ISBN: 9781409308058
RRP: £4.99

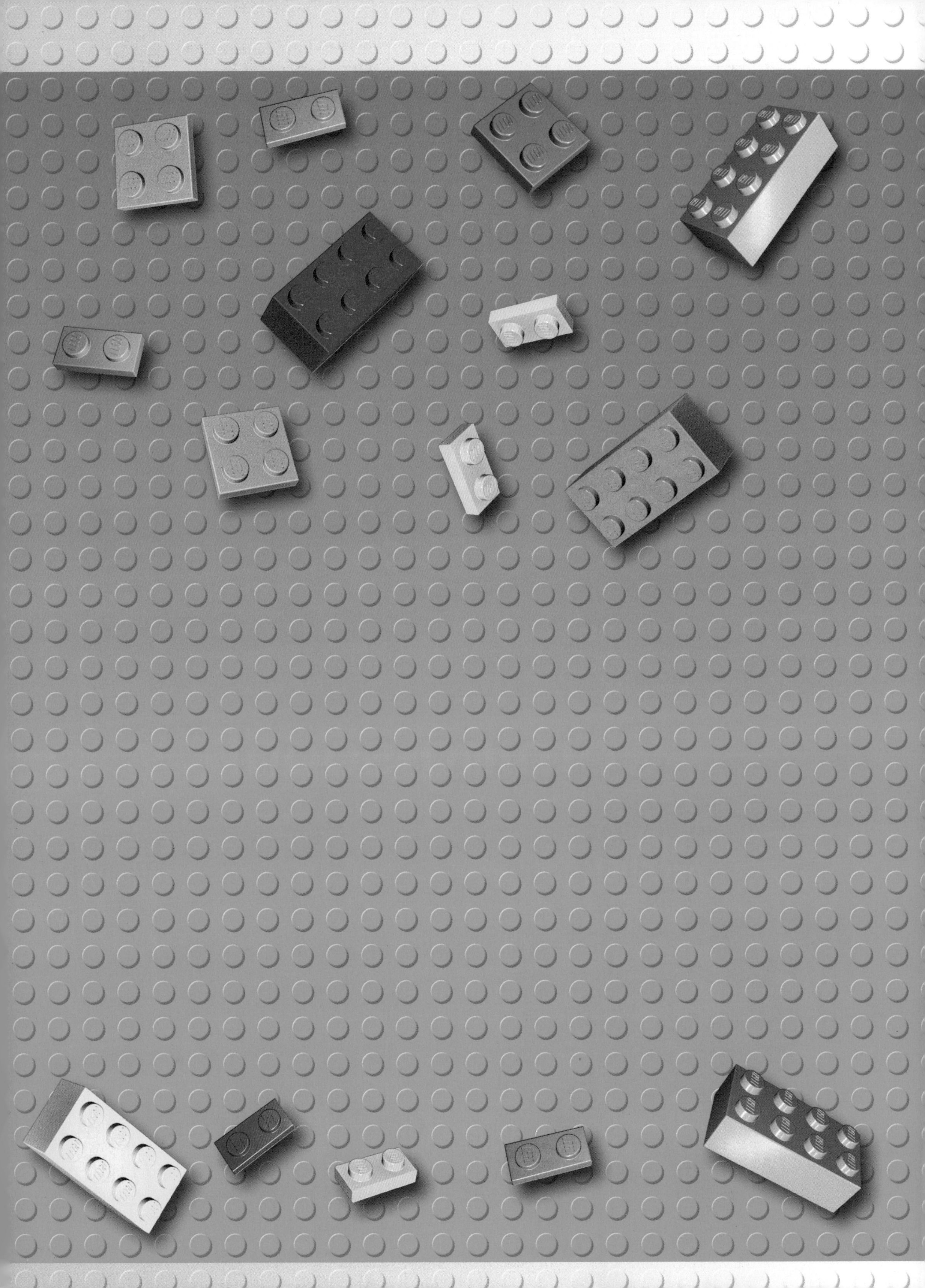